to Ulf and Lucy

May these tender
sentiments inspire
and comfort you

George & Mary

THE
TOM LEHRER
SONG BOOK

THE
TOM LEHRER
SONG BOOK

by Tom Lehrer

Introduction by AL CAPP

Illustrated by GRISHA DOTZENKO

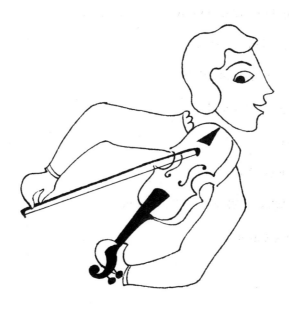

CROWN PUBLISHERS, Inc. • NEW YORK

Table of Contents

Copyright, 1952, 1953, 1954, by Tom Lehrer

Library of Congress Catalogue Card Number: 54-12068

Manufactured in the U. S. A.

Second Printing, December 1954

INTRODUCTION

The advantage of this book of Tom Lehrer's songs over his record album (and I assume you have one) is that you are spared his voice.

Tom Lehrer's is not an unpleasant voice — it is an offended voice. This is not surprising, though, for his is an offended spirit.

He is offended by ideas that we have accepted unquestioningly all our lives, perhaps with secret misgivings but without protest. Tom Lehrer here protests. And that is not surprising either, because, since he was a student and teacher at Harvard when these songs were written, he hadn't much else to do.

His displeasure with the universal and practically sacred notion that two young, lovely, glowing people, who love each other for their youth and loveliness and glow, will continue to be enthralled by each other long after they both wrinkle, balloon, and sag, caused Tom Lehrer to write one of the world's most depressing love songs, "When You Are Old and Gray" ("I'll hate you"). I have seen this one throw a formerly gay and laughing group into suicidal gloom.

To counteract the theory presented in many a popular song that all home towns are heaven, Lehrer has written "My Home Town," a disconcerting description of what you get if you do go back to any place you've had the good sense to leave. In "I Wanna Go Back to Dixie" he restricts his fire to the South as a homeland, with socially conscious overtones (not sufficiently conscious, though, to spoil the humor). His feelings about all Boy Scouts are expressed in "Be Prepared," which enlarges on that admonition to include more fundamental rules of conduct than the Boy Scout Handbook bothers to mention.

There are also protests against folk songs, football, hunting, the radioactive West, and other aspects of the "American" way of life. They are cast in the form of takeoffs on various popular song forms, but they satirize more than the mere song forms themselves.

In this book you will find dismay and despair to suit every prejudice. Tom Lehrer is a disillusioned spirit, and let us all be grateful for that.

AL CAPP

Cambridge, Mass.
1954

The Hunting Song

Words and Music by
TOM LEHRER

wardens, seven hunters, and a cow. I was in no mood to trifle, I took down my trusty rifle And went out to stalk my prey. What a haul I made that day! I tied them to my fender and I drove them home somehow, Two game wardens, seven hunters, and a cow.

The law was ver-y firm, it Took a-way my per- mit, The worst pun-ish-ment I ev- er en- dured._____ It turned out there was a rea - son, Cows were out of sea - son, And one of the hunt-ers was- n't in - sured._____ Peo-ple ask me how I

The Irish Ballad

Words and Music by
TOM LEHRER

Her mother she could never stand,
    Sing rickety-tickety-tin,
Her mother she could never stand,
And so a cyanide soup she planned.
The mother died with the spoon in her hand,
    And her face in a hideous grin, a grin,
    Her face in a hideous grin.

She set her sister's hair on fire,
    Sing rickety-tickety-tin,
She set her sister's hair on fire,
And as the smoke and flame rose high'r,
Danced around the funeral pyre,
    Playing a violin, -olin,
    Playing a violin.

She weighted her brother down with stones,
    Sing rickety-tickety-tin,
She weighted her brother down with stones,
And sent him off to Davy Jones.
All they ever found were some bones,
    And occasional pieces of skin, of skin,
    Occasional pieces of skin.

One day when she had nothing to do,
    Sing rickety-tickety-tin,
One day when she had nothing to do,
She cut her baby brother in two,
And served him up as an Irish stew,
    And invited the neighbors in, -bors in,
    Invited the neighbors in.

And when at last the police came by,
    Sing rickety-tickety-tin,
And when at last the police came by,
Her little pranks she did not deny.
To do so, she would have had to lie,
    And lying, she knew, was a sin, a sin,
    Lying, she knew, was a sin.

My tragic tale I won't prolong,
    Sing rickety-tickety-tin,
My tragic tale I won't prolong,
And if you do not enjoy my song,
You've yourselves to blame if it's too long,
    You should never have let me begin,
    begin,
    You should never have let me begin.

13

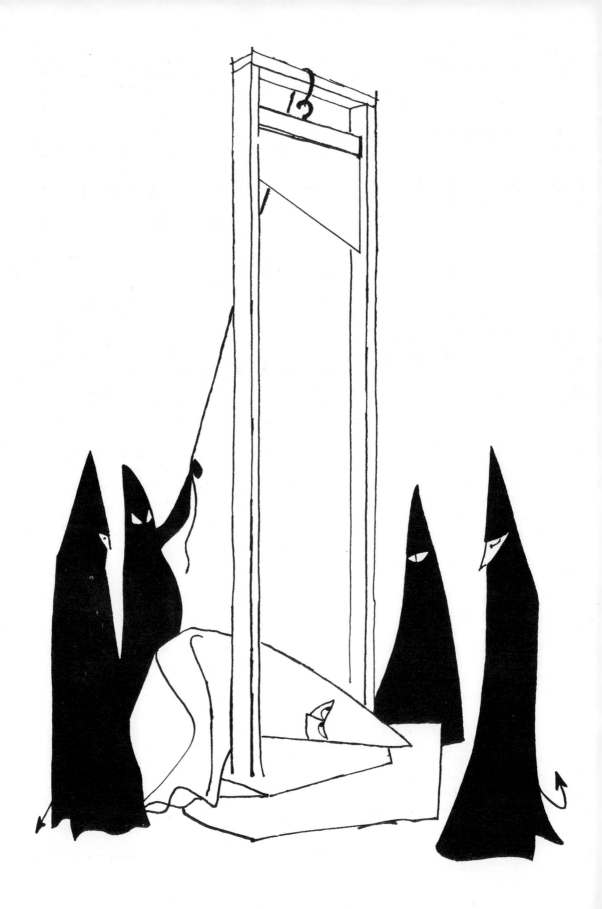

I Wanna Go Back to Dixie

Words and Music by
TOM LEHRER

wait-in' for the Rob-ert E. Lee. ___ (It was nev-er there on time.) I'll

go back to the Swa-nee, Where pel - lag-ra makes you scraw-ny, And the

hon-ey-suck-le clut-ters up the vine. _____ I

real-ly am a - fix-in' To go home and start a - mix-in' Down be-

talk with south - ern gen - tle - men And put my white sheet

on a - gain, I ain't seen one good lynch - in' in years.

The land of the boll wee - vil, Where the

laws are me - di - e - val, Is call - in' me to come and nev - er more

19

My Home Town

Words and Music by
TOM LEHRER

1. I real - ly have a yen To go back once a - gain, Back
(2. The) guy that taught us math, Who nev - er took a bath, Ac -

to the place where no one wears a frown, _____ To see once
quired a cer - tain meas - ure of re - nown, _____ And aft - er

*A small prize is being offered by the author to the reader who suggests the most imaginative line to be inserted at this point. (The original line is omitted for several reasons.)

23

free   in   my   home   town. _____ I re‐mem‐ber

___   in   my   home   town. _____ I re‐mem‐ber

Dan, _____ the   drug‐gist on the cor‐ner, 'e ___ Was

Sam, _____ he   was   the vil‐lage id‐i‐ot, ___ And

nev‐er mean or or‐ner‐y, ___ He was   swell. _____ He killed his

though it seems a pit‐y it ___ Was ___ so. _____ He loved to

moth‐er‐in‐law and ground her up   real   well,   And

burn ___ down hous‐es just   to watch the   glow,   And

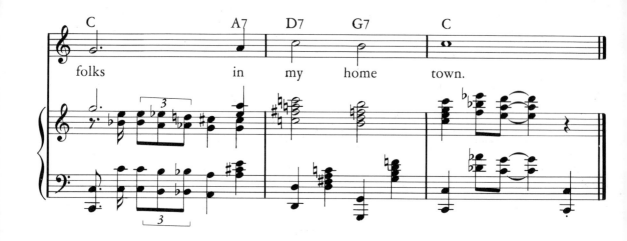

folks   in   my   home   town.

When You Are Old and Gray

Words and Music by
TOM LEHRER

Arirang

Korean
FOLK SONGS

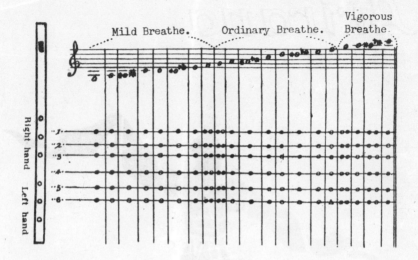

Mild Breathe.   Ordinary Breathe.   Vigorous Breathe.

Right hand   Left hand

아 리 랑

1. 아리랑 아리랑 아라리요
   아리랑 고개로 넘어간다
   나를 버리고 가시는 임은
   십리도 못가서 발병난다.
2. 아리랑 아리랑 아라리요
   아리랑 고개를 넘어 간다
   청천 하늘엔 별도 많고
   이 내 가슴엔 수심도 많다

ARIRANG

1. Arirang Arirang Arariyo
   O'er the Arirang Hill going thou art,
   If thou leave here deserting me,
   Will have a footsore within a mile.
2. Arirang Arirang Arariyo,
   O'er the Arirang Hill going thou art,
   So many stars are twinkling in the sky,
   So many sighs within my heart.

아 리 랑
ARIRANG

李 興 烈 編曲
Lee, Hung-Yul

1. 아 리 랑— 아 리 랑— 아 라 리— 요 ――― 아 리 랑— 고 개 로—
   Ah ri rang— Ah ri rang Ah rah ri— yo ――― Ah rirang— ko ge ro—

2. 아 리 랑— 아 리 랑— 아 라 리— 요 ――― 아 리 랑— 고 개 로—
   Ah ri rang— Ah rirang ah rah ri— yo ――― Ah— ri rang— ko ge ro—

넘 어 간 다 나 를 버 리 고 가 시 는 넘—
num u kahn dah Nah rul bu ri go kah shinunnim—

넘 어 간 다 청 천 하 늘 엔 별 도— 많—
num u kahn dah Chung chun hah nul en pyul do— mahn—

은 심 리 도— 못 가 서— 발 벙 난 다
un shim ri do mot ga su— bal pyungnahn tah

고 이— 내 가 숨 엔 수 심 도 많 다
ko i — ne ka— sumen — soosim-do mahn tah

Explanatory Remarks

ARIRANG

Under Japanese pressure. We shed tears of national indignation singing Arirang and now swear to realize our wishes singing this warmhearted song.

Wherever Koreans are, the lovely melody of this song which stands aloof from love, spite, happiness and sadness is sure to be heard.

Every foreigner who has been in this country associates Korea with this song. To that extent, this song is famous and the melody popular.

It is not without good reason that this song should meet with public favor that is to say, coincides with our national emotions and concurs with current ideas.

The history of the origin of Arirang is various and the melodies arranged by each district are respectively different.

"Ponjo = Original", so called, is the most popular melody which is known even is many foreign countries. Beside this, there are Miryang-Arirang, Kang-Won-Arirang, Chung-Sun-Arirang, Keen Arirang, New-Arirang, and Arirang World etc.

It is said that the song of Arirang originated from the time when Tae-won-goon, the father of the last king of the Lee-Dynasty, was rebuilding the Kyungbock Palace, but it is though. that this might be the most popular one of the many various Arirang melodies. The melancho'y melody of this song which consists of four phrases, time signature of $\frac{3}{4}$, moderato, seems to symbolize the sorrowful and painful fortune of our nation.

We can not overlook that this melody holds firmness of purpose desiring final victory against the enemy through national trials and tribulations.

Realizing that this melody is frankly reflected in the modern history of Korea, everybody will give assent as to how suitable this song is for the Korean people even though there are some who dislike its having grief and lack of spirit.

Sung Ha Trading Co., Ltd.
P. O. Box 1166
Seoul, Korea

INTERLUDE

aw – ful de – bil – i – ty, a less-ened u – til – i – ty, a loss of mo – bil – i – ty is a strong pos – si – bil – i – ty, In all pro – ba – bil – i – ty I'll lose my vi – ril – i – ty and you your fer – til – i – ty and de – sir – a – bil – i – ty, And this li – a –

I Hold Your Hand in Mine

Words and Music by
TOM LEHRER

Tenderly, with feeling

I hold your hand in mine, dear, I press it to my lips. _____ I

take a health y bite from your

dain - ty fin - ger - tips._____ My

joy would be com - plete, dear, if

you were on - ly here,_____ But still I

keep your hand as a pre-cious sou-ve-
nir. _____ The night you died I cut it
off, I real-ly don't know why. _____ For
now each time I kiss it, _____ I get blood-stains

on my tie. _____ I'm sor - ry

now I killed you, _____ for our love was some - thing

fine. _____ And till they come to get me,

I shall hold your hand in mine. _____

The Wiener Schnitzel Waltz

Words and Music by
TOM LEHRER

Liltingly

1. Do you re - mem - ber the night I held you so
(2. Oh, I re -) mem - ber the night I held you so

tight, As we danced to the Wie-ner Schnit-zel Waltz.
tight, As we danced to the Wie-ner Schnit-zel Waltz.

The mu-sic was gay, and the set-ting was Vi-en-nese, Your
Your lips were like wine (if you'll par-don the sim-i-le), The

hair wore some ros-es (or per-haps they were pe-o-nies). I was
mu-sic was love-ly and quite Ru-dolf Frim-l-y. I drank

blind to your ob-vi-ous faults, As we
wine, you drank choc-o-late malts, And we

danced 'cross the scene To the strains of the Wien-er Schnit-zel Waltz.
both turned quite green To the strains of the Wien-er Schnit-zel

1. To Interlude

INTERLUDE

Oh, I drank some cham-pagne from your shoe. _____ I was drunk by the time I got through. _____ For I did-n't know, as I raised that cup, It had

Fight Fiercely, Harvard!

Words and Music by
TOM LEHRER

Be Prepared

Words and Music by
TOM LEHRER

1. Be pre - pared! _____ That's the Boy Scouts' marching song, Be pre-
(2. Be pre-) pared! _____ That's the Boy Scouts' so-lemn creed, Be pre-

pared! _____ As through life you march a - long. Be pre-pared to hold your
pared! _____ And be clean in word and deed. Don't so - li - cit for your

they will not be found, And be care-ful not to smoke them when the
new and dif-f'rent kind, And you come a-cross a Girl Scout who is

scout-mas-ter's a - round, For he on - ly will in - sist that they be
si - mi - lar - ly in - clined, Don't be ner-vous, don't be flus-tered, don't be

shared. _____ Be pre - pared! _____
scared. _____ Be pre - pared! _____

2. Be pre -

49

The Old Dope Peddler

Words and Music by
TOM LEHRER

When the shades of night are

The Wild West is Where I Want to Be

Words and Music by
TOM LEHRER

Moderately

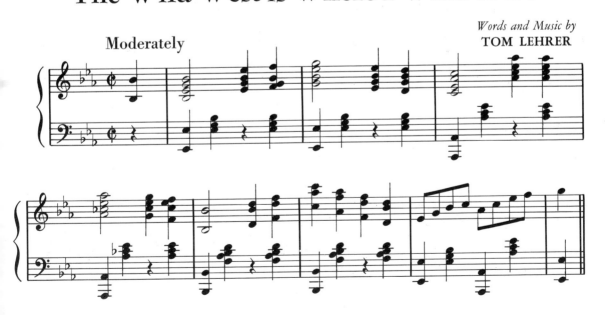

'Mid the sagebrush and the cac- tus I'll watch the fel- lers prac- tice Drop-pin' bombs through the clean de- sert breeze. ___ I'll have on my som - bre- ro And of course I'll wear a pair o' Le - vis o - ver my lead B. V. D's. ___

I will leave the cit-y's rush, Leave the fan-cy and the plush, Leave the snow and leave the slush, And the crowds.

I will seek the de-sert's hush, Where the scen-er-y is lush, How I long to see the mush-room clouds.

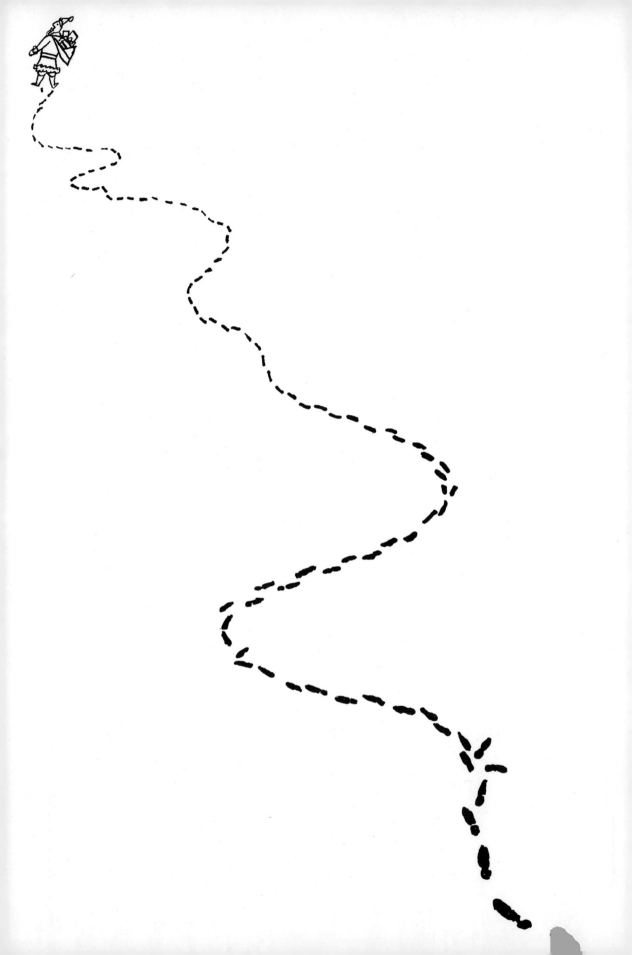

A Christmas Carol

Words and Music by
TOM LEHRER

Merrily

1. Christ-mas time is here, by gol-ly, Dis-ap-pro-val would be fol-ly,
(2. Re-) la-tions, spar-ing no ex-pense, 'll Send some use-less old u-ten-sil,

Deck the halls with hunks of hol-ly, Fill the cup and don't say when.
Or a match-ing pen and pen-cil. ("Just the thing I need! How nice!")It

Kill the tur-keys, ducks, and chick-ens, Mix the punch, drag out the Dick-ens,
does-n't mat-ter how sin-cere it Is, nor how heart-felt the spir-it,

E - ven though the pros - pect sick - ens, Bro - ther, here we go a - gain. On
Sen - ti - ment will not en - dear it, What's im - por - tant

Christ-mas Day you can't get sore, Your fel - low man you must a - dore, There's

time to cheat him all the more, The oth - er three hun-dred and six-ty-four. 2. Re-

is the price. Hark, the Her - ald Trib-une sings, Ad - ver - tis - ing